C000132735

Flute Exam Pieces

ABRSM Grade 1

Selected from the 2014–2017 syllabus

Name

Date of exam

Contents

Footnotes: Anthony Burton

Other pieces for Grade 1

First published in 2013 by ABRSM (Publishing) Ltd, a wholly owned subsidiary of ABRSM, 24 Portland Place, London W1B 1LU, United Kingdom © 2013 by The Associated Board of the Royal Schools of Music

Music origination by Andrew Jones Cover by Kate Benjamin & Andy Potts Printed in England by Caligraving Ltd, Thetford, Norfolk Reprinted in 2014

MIX
Paper from responsible sources
FSC™ C109619

A:1

Minuetto

Second movement from Sonata in E flat, Op. 99 No. 3

Arranged by Peter Wastall

James Hook
(1746–1827)

James Hook was born in Norwich, in the east of England, and was playing harpsichord concertos in public by the age of six. He later moved to London, where he worked as an organist, teacher and composer. His songs became popular in the fashionable pleasure gardens of the time, and he was appointed organist and composer first to Marylebone Gardens and then to Vauxhall Gardens, where he remained for more than 45 years. He was one of the first English musicians to perform on the piano, which was gradually replacing the harpsichord. This piece in the dance form of the minuet was published in London in 1803 as the last of *Three sonatas for the Piano Forte with an accompaniment for a German flute or Violin*. This was a customary description of music for a melody instrument and keyboard in this period. 'German flute' meant the transverse flute as opposed to the recorder.

AB 3677

Flute Exam Pieces

ABRSM Grade 1

Selected from the 2014–2017 syllabus

Piano accompaniment

Contents

Footnotes: Anthony Burton

The pieces in this album have been taken from a variety of different sources. Where appropriate, they have been checked with original source material and edited to help the player when preparing for performance. Ornament realizations have been added, as have the metronome marks shown within square brackets. Details of other editorial amendments or suggestions are given in the footnotes. Breath marks (retained here where they appear in the source edition) and all editorial additions are for guidance only; they are not comprehensive or obligatory. Descriptive titles are given in their original language, and translations into English appear above the footnotes.

ABRSM Flute Exams: requirements

Pieces
In the exam, candidates must play three pieces, one chosen from each of the three syllabus lists (A, B and C). Candidates are free to choose from the pieces printed in this album and/or from the other pieces set for the grade: a full list is given in the flute part with this score as well as in the 2014–2017 Woodwind syllabus.

Scales and arpeggios
Sight-reading
Aural tests
} Full details are available online at www.abrsm.org/flute1 or in the 2014–2017 Woodwind syllabus booklet.

First published in 2013 by ABRSM (Publishing) Ltd, a wholly owned subsidiary of ABRSM, 24 Portland Place, London W1B 1LU, United Kingdom
© 2013 by The Associated Board of the Royal Schools of Music

Music origination by Andrew Jones
Cover by Kate Benjamin & Andy Potts
Printed in England by Caligraving Ltd, Thetford, Norfolk
Reprinted in 2014

Minuetto

Second movement from Sonata in E flat, Op. 99 No. 3

Arranged by Peter Wastall

James Hook
(1746–1827)

James Hook was born in Norwich, in the east of England, and was playing harpsichord concertos in public by the age of six. He later moved to London, where he worked as an organist, teacher and composer. His songs became popular in the fashionable pleasure gardens of the time, and he was appointed organist and composer first to Marylebone Gardens and then to Vauxhall Gardens, where he remained for more than 45 years. He was one of the first English musicians to perform on the piano, which was gradually replacing the harpsichord. This piece in the dance form of the minuet was published in London in 1803 as the last of *Three sonatas for the Piano Forte with an accompaniment for a German flute or Violin*. This was a customary description of music for a melody instrument and keyboard in this period. 'German flute' meant the transverse flute as opposed to the recorder.

AB 3677

Rigaudon
Z. 653

A:2

Arranged by Hugh Stuart

Henry Purcell
(1659–95)

The rigaudon is a dance of southern French origin, which became popular at the court in Paris in the later 17th century, and also in London. This example is by the great English composer Henry Purcell, and was published in 1689 – under the title 'Riggadoon' – in an anthology of keyboard pieces called *The Second Part of Musick's Hand-Maid*. Purcell's original is in ¢ or 2/2 time, which suggests a brisk tempo for this arrangement; although the arranger's metronome mark is ♩ = 112, students may prefer a brisker tempo of ♩ = c.138.

The Rakes o' Mallow

Arranged by Ian Denley

Trad. Irish

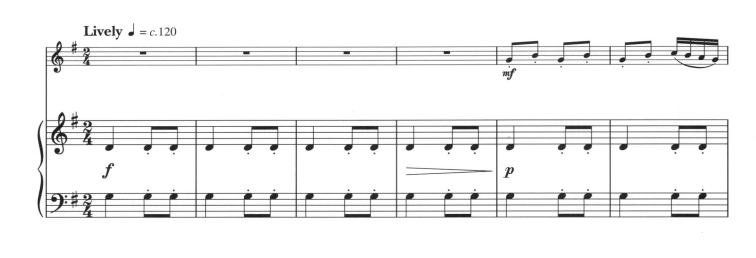

'The Rakes o' Mallow' is an Irish folksong in dance rhythm, first printed in London in the first half of the 18th century. Its lyrics describe the rowdy behaviour of the 'rakes', or dissolute young men, of the town of Mallow in County Cork. In this arrangement by Ian Denley, from his collection *Time Pieces for Flute*, Volume 1, the piano part imitates the sustained drones of bagpipes. Although the arranger's metronome mark is ♩ = *c*.120, students may prefer a more relaxed tempo of ♩ = *c*.100.

© 1998 by The Associated Board of the Royal Schools of Music
Reproduced from *Time Pieces for Flute*, Volume 1, selected and arranged by Ian Denley (ABRSM)

Lupin, the Pot-Bellied Pig

No. 9 from *The First Amos Flute Album*

Keith Amos
(born 1939)

B:1

Keith Amos has had a busy career as a composer, arranger and conductor. He wrote *Lupin, the Pot-Bellied Pig* in 1996 as a story for narrator and orchestra and later arranged the accompaniment for wind band, for flute choir and for wind quintet; the latter version was the source of this arrangement. The story was inspired by an encounter with the title character on the remote and beautiful island of Sark, in the Channel Islands off the south coast of England. Lupin has her own song, a jaunty tune which is sung and whistled during the piece: it begins 'This is the story of a pot-bellied pig', and includes her name sung to the two two-bar phrases at bar 17. This version for flute and piano comes from *The First Amos Flute Album*.

B:2

Guanabara Bay

No. 1 from *Flute Globetrotters*

Ros Stephen
(born 1972)

Ros Stephen is a violinist, a founder member of the popular tango ensemble Tango Siempre, and also a composer and arranger. Her *Flute Globetrotters* album consists of original melodies in styles from different parts of the world. Brazil is represented at the beginning of the volume by 'Guanabara Bay', in the tempo of the bossa nova. This is a style of Brazilian music which became popular in the 1960s, a type of samba with an intricate syncopated rhythm often running across a pair of bars. This piece is named after the bay on which the Brazilian seaside city of Rio de Janeiro stands, and was conceived as a song, with words (you can sing them to the flute part) beginning:

On a starlit night we walk on Guanabara Bay
while the ocean gently whispers on the sand.
A samba band is playing; music takes our cares away.
I hope it never ends, the music never ends.

Edelweiss

from *The Sound of Music*

Arranged by Donald Thomson

Richard Rodgers (1902–79) **and**
Oscar Hammerstein II (1895–1960)

The Sound of Music is one of the most successful musicals by the partnership of Richard Rodgers, who wrote the music, and Oscar Hammerstein II, who wrote the lyrics. It was first produced on Broadway in New York in 1959 and ran for more than three and a half years; it was made into a film in 1965. The story is based on a real-life group of child singers, members of the von Trapp family, in Austria in the late 1930s, and their escape from the Nazi army of occupation. The song 'Edelweiss', in waltz time, is sung by the children's father at a music festival. It is about a flower that is native to the Austrian mountains, and so it is a demonstration of patriotic feelings. This arrangement presents the song without phrasing; players may wish to add some of their own.

Rigaudon

Z. 653

Arranged by Hugh Stuart

Henry Purcell
(1659–95)

A:2

The rigaudon is a dance of southern French origin, which became popular at the court in Paris in the later 17th century, and also in London. This example is by the great English composer Henry Purcell, and was published in 1689 – under the title 'Riggadoon' – in an anthology of keyboard pieces called *The Second Part of Musick's Hand-Maid*. Purcell's original is in ₵ or 2/2 time, which suggests a brisk tempo for this arrangement; although the arranger's metronome mark is ♩ = 112, students may prefer a brisker tempo of ♩ = *c*.138.

The Rakes o' Mallow

Arranged by Ian Denley

Trad. Irish

'The Rakes o' Mallow' is an Irish folksong in dance rhythm, first printed in London in the first half of the 18th century. Its lyrics describe the rowdy behaviour of the 'rakes', or dissolute young men, of the town of Mallow in County Cork. In this arrangement by Ian Denley, from his collection *Time Pieces for Flute*, Volume 1, the piano part imitates the sustained drones of bagpipes. Although the arranger's metronome mark is ♩ = *c*.120, students may prefer a more relaxed tempo of ♩ = *c*.100.

Lupin, the Pot-Bellied Pig

No. 9 from *The First Amos Flute Album*

B:1

Keith Amos
(born 1939)

Keith Amos has had a busy career as a composer, arranger and conductor. He wrote *Lupin, the Pot-Bellied Pig* in 1996 as a story for narrator and orchestra and later arranged the accompaniment for wind band, for flute choir and for wind quintet; the latter version was the source of this arrangement. The story was inspired by an encounter with the title character on the remote and beautiful island of Sark, in the Channel Islands off the south coast of England. Lupin has her own song, a jaunty tune which is sung and whistled during the piece: it begins 'This is the story of a pot-bellied pig', and includes her name sung to the two two-bar phrases at bar 17. This version for flute and piano comes from *The First Amos Flute Album*.

B:2

Guanabara Bay

No. 1 from *Flute Globetrotters*

Ros Stephen
(born 1972)

Ros Stephen is a violinist, a founder member of the popular tango ensemble Tango Siempre, and also a composer and arranger. Her *Flute Globetrotters* album consists of original melodies in styles from different parts of the world. Brazil is represented at the beginning of the volume by 'Guanabara Bay', in the tempo of the bossa nova. This is a style of Brazilian music which became popular in the 1960s, a type of samba with an intricate syncopated rhythm often running across a pair of bars. This piece is named after the bay on which the Brazilian seaside city of Rio de Janeiro stands, and was conceived as a song, with words (you can sing them to the flute part) beginning:

> On a starlit night we walk on Guanabara Bay
> while the ocean gently whispers on the sand.
> A samba band is playing; music takes our cares away.
> I hope it never ends, the music never ends.

Edelweiss

from *The Sound of Music*

 B:3

Arranged by Donald Thomson

Richard Rodgers (1902–79) and
Oscar Hammerstein II (1895–1960)

The Sound of Music is one of the most successful musicals by the partnership of Richard Rodgers, who wrote the music, and Oscar Hammerstein II, who wrote the lyrics. It was first produced on Broadway in New York in 1959 and ran for more than three and a half years; it was made into a film in 1965. The story is based on a real-life group of child singers, members of the von Trapp family, in Austria in the late 1930s, and their escape from the Nazi army of occupation. The song 'Edelweiss', in waltz time, is sung by the children's father at a music festival. It is about a flower that is native to the Austrian mountains, and so it is a demonstration of patriotic feelings. This arrangement presents the song without phrasing; players may wish to add some of their own.

Jazz Waltz

C:1

Nikki Iles
(born 1963)

Nikki Iles is one of Britain's leading jazz pianists and composers. She leads her own quintet and trio, and has also performed and recorded with the singers Tina May and Norma Winstone, the Kenny Wheeler Big Band and other prominent jazz soloists and groups. She has composed for the dancer and choreographer Mimi Cichanowicz and the London Philharmonic Orchestra's contemporary group Renga. She has been a member of the team developing the ABRSM jazz syllabus, and has written this study in jazz waltz time specially for this album. Her suggestions for performing it read: 'Try to make the staccato notes really short to emphasize the contrast between the phrases with crotchets and the phrases with smoother jazz quavers. This will help give the piece more character.'

© 2013 by The Associated Board of the Royal Schools of Music

Exercise in G

No. 30 from *Schule für Flöte*, Part 1

C:2

Edited by Maximilian Schwedler

Ernesto Köhler
(1849–1907)

Schule für Flöte Flute Method

Ernesto Köhler was an Italian-born flautist who spent the last 36 years of his life playing in the St Petersburg opera orchestra. He composed over 100 works for the flute, including sets of studies and a teaching method *Schule für Flöte*. The latter is the source of this study in playing in a singing style. The *mp* dynamic in bar 1 is a suggestion for exam purposes only.

© by Musikverlag Zimmerman, Frankfurt am Main
Reproduced by permission of Peters Edition Ltd, London. All enquiries about this piece, apart from those directly relating to the exams, should be addressed to Peters Edition Ltd, 2–6 Baches Street, London N1 6DN.

C:3

Itchy Feet

from *Flute Salad*

Oliver Ledbury
(born 1963)

The British composer Oliver Ledbury studied at the University of Bristol and the Guildhall School of Music & Drama in London. He has written music for films and television programmes, including several natural history series, as well as various educational pieces. His *Flute Salad*, published in 1994 and named with a pun on the familiar dessert fruit salad, has been described as 'a rich, colourful and fruity selection of solos for the early–intermediate flute soloist'. The first piece in the collection is 'Itchy Feet', a title suggesting restlessness. For the exam the grace note arpeggio in the last bar is optional.